MULTIPLE-CHOICE

MATHS

Practice Test 13

Guidance for completing this Test.

1. Read the questions carefully.

2. Do your working out thoroughly.

3. Read your answers carefully.

4. Choose what you think is the correct answer carefully.

5. Underline or circle the answer, immediately after the question.

6. Transfer the LETTER **A,B,C,D or E** to the answer sheet.

7. Make sure to mark the answer box like [—] not [╱].

8. Check carefully that you have transferred your correct answer.

9 . This test lasts for **45 minutes.**

PUPIL'S NAME _____

TOTAL MARK (Out of 45)	

MATHS (Multiple Choice)   Test 13.

Question 1.   Change **4350 millilitres** into litres.

A.   4 litres   B.   4.3 litres   C.   43.5 litres
D.   4.35 litres   E.   435 litres

Question 2.   Change **5250 millimetres** into metres.

A.   5.25 metres   B.   0.525 metres   C.   52.5 metres
D.   525 metres   E.   5 metres

Question 3.

This is a solid shape.

All the corners are
right angles.

What is the **volume**
of the solid in **cubic cms** ?

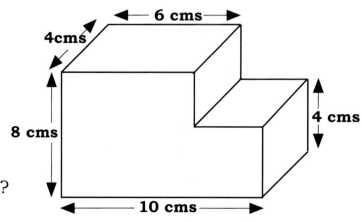

A.   192   B.   320   C.   256   D.   64   E.   32

Question 4.

In this magic square the **SUMS**
of all horizontal, vertical and
diagonal lines of numbers have
the **same total**.

0.5	2.25	1
?	1.25	0.75
1.5	0.25	2

What number is missing ?

A.   0.5   B.   1.25   C.   0.25   D.   2.25   E.   1.75

1.

Question 5.   Work out the answer to this calculation :-

455 millimetres + 23.7 cms + 0.38 metres = _____ **mms**

Give your answer in millimetres.

A. 1072   B. 10720   C. 107.2   D. 10.72   E. 107200

Question 6.   What is the **average price** of 4 cars which cost

£6400   £7620   £8060   £6640

A. £7010   B. £7350   C.   £7180   D. £7840   E. £7260

Question 7.   How many less than **600** is **20 squared** ?

A. 400   B. 580   C. 100   D. 1000   E. 200

Question 8.   If Fred is facing **North-west**
and turns **180° anticlockwise**
in which direction
is he now facing ?

A.   North-east   B.   West   C.   South
D.   South-east   E.   South-west

Question 9.   A packet of cereal weighs **2.4 kgs.**
A child's serving of cereal is **30 grams.**
How many children will get **one serving**
each out of the **2.4 kg** packet ?

A.   40   B.   60   C.   80   D.   100   E.   24

2.

Question 10. In a bag there are **3 blue** balls, **4 red** balls and **6 green** balls. A ball is taken out of the bag at random. Which word or words best describe the probability that a **green** ball will be picked ?

A. less than evens   B. more than evens   C. certain
D. impossible   E very likely

Questions 11 & 12.

There are **240** cars in a car park.

The Pie chart shows how many

of each colour there were.

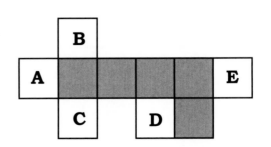

Question 11. How many **silver** cars were there ?

A. 120   B. 60   C. 36
D. 72   E. 80

Question 12. What size is the angle marked **X** ? ___

A. 30°   B. 60°   C. 90°   D. 120°   E. 72°

Question 13. The **grey squares** are part of the net of a cube.

Which **white square** would complete the net ?

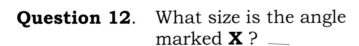

Question 14.   **56.7 ÷ _____ = 0.567**

What number is missing ?

A. 100   B. 1000   C. 10   D. 1   E. 20

Question 15.

The **length** of one side of

this square is **2q**.

What is the perimeter of the square ?

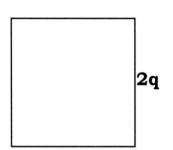

2q

A.   2q + 4   B.   6q   C.   8q   D.   4q   E.   16q

Question 16.   The **Average** weight of **5 girls** is **27 kgs.**

The Weights of **4** of the girls are :-

22 . 8 kgs.   29 . 5 kgs.   30 . 4 kgs. and 25 kgs.

The weight of the **5th girl** is:-

A. 27.3 kg   B. 28.1 kg   C. 27.7 kg   D. 26.3 kg   E. 28.3 kg

---

Question 17.

What number is missing

from this calculation ?

$$
\begin{array}{ccc}
\square & \square & \square \\
x & & 6 \\
\hline
7 & 1 & 4
\end{array}
$$

A.   147   B.   720   C.   4284   D.   119   E.   102

Question 18.

Three of the vertices of a square
are marked on the grid.

What are the co-ordinates of
the **fourth** vertex ?

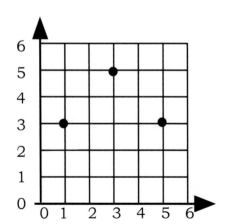

A. (1, 1)   B. (2, 2)   C. (3, 3)   D. (3, 1)   E. (1, 3)

4.

Question 19. A new car showroom opened in **2006** and in that first year they sold **246** cars.

In **2007** they sold **twice** as many as in 2006 while in **2008** they sold **twice** as many as in 2007.

How many cars were sold in **2008** ?

A.   246   B.   492   C.   738   D.   1968   E. 984

Question 20. Boys' trousers are sold in **three** sizes, small, medium and large.

24% of these were small and **37%** were medium.

What percentage of the trousers were large ?

A.   39%   B.   49%   C.   29%   D.   63%   E.   76%

Question 21. The **lowest** temperature recorded in the Arctic was **-68°C**.

In the Summer the temperature would rise by **40°C**.

What would the Summer temperature be ?

A.   28°C   B.   -40°C   C.   68°C   D.   -28°C   E.   108°C

Question 22. The numbers **3** and **7** are **factors** of :-

A.   45   B.   42   C.   24   D.   49   E.   35

Question 23. Paint takes between **3 and a half** and **5 hours** to dry. John finishes painting a wall at **5.30 pm**.

What was the **earliest time** by which the paint would be dry ?

A. 9.00 am   B. 10.30 pm   C. 8.30 pm   D. 9.30 pm   E. 9.00 pm

Question 24. The total cost of the contents of

Mary's shopping basket is **£34.65**.

She has vouchers to the value of **£5.80** to be deducted.

How much did Mary have to pay ?

A. £40.45   B. £28.85   C. £5.80   D. £34.65   E. £18.85

Question 25.

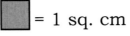 = 1 sq. cm

Each square on the grid measures **1cm by 1cm**.

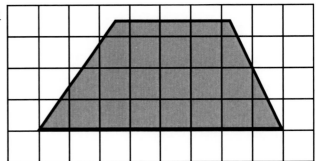

What is the **best estimate** of the area of this shape ?

A.   22 sq.cm   B.   13 sq.cm   C.   28 sq.cm
D.   40 sq.cm   E.   14 sq.cm

Question 26.   Which group of numbers below are **multiples of both 5 and 6 ?**

A.   25, 30, 36   B.   20, 30, 40   C.   60, 30, 90
D.   36, 48, 60   E.   15, 18, 20

Question 27.   Apples cost **53 pence** each. Adam bought **168** apples.

He wants to work out the approximate cost of the apples.

The calculation which gives an answer **closest** to the **exact** answer is :-

A.   160 x 50 p   B.   160 x 60 p   C.   170 x 60 p
D.   170 x 50 p   E.   200 x 50 p

6.

Question 28.

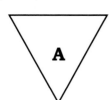

Which of the shapes has **more than THREE** lines of symmetry ?

Question 29.   Jack and Andy are on a see-saw.

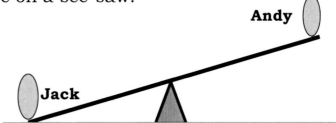

Jack's weight is
41.5 kgs while Andy
weighs **36.7 kgs.**

What weight needs to be added to Andy's
side to **balance** the see-saw ?

A.   36.7 kg   B.   41.5 kg   C.   78.2 kg   D.   5.2 kg   E. 4.8 kg

---

Question 30.   Of the **60** oranges in a box **24** are **not** ripe.

What fraction are **ripe** ?

A. $\frac{3}{5}$ B. $\frac{1}{4}$ C. $\frac{1}{3}$ D. $\frac{2}{5}$ E. $\frac{5}{6}$

Question 31.   How many times is the **9** in **8.09** less than

the **9** in the number **79.3** ?

A.   1   B.   100   C.   10   D.   1000   E.   70

Question 32.   How many **litres** in **8055** millilitres ?

A.   0.8055   B.   80.55   C.   805.5   D.   8055   E.   8.055

Question 33. The following calculation is carried out by a class of P.6 pupils.

> **Multiply 83 by 40 and then subtract 9**

Which of the following calculations would give the **correct answer** ?

A.   83 x 31   B.   80 x 40 - 9   C.   83 x 10 x 4 - 9
D.   80 x 40 + 9 x 40 - 9   E.   83 - 9 x 40

Questions 34 & 35..   The squares on the grid are **1 cm by 1 cm.**

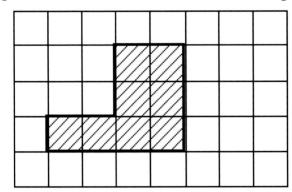
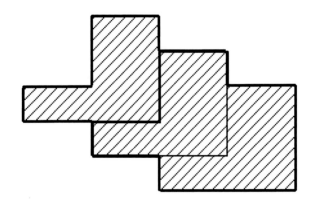

The grid shows an irregular shape.

Three of these are joined together without overlapping.

Question 34.   What is the **perimeter** of this **joined-up pattern** ?

A. 14 cms   B.   28 cms   C.   42 cms   D.   26 cms   E.   48 cms

Question 35.   What is the **area** of the joined-up pattern ?

A. 24 sq.cms   B. 8 sq.cms   C. 16 sq.cms   D. 6 sq.cms   E. 26 sq.cms

---

Question 36.   As a **whole number** what is the size of

the **largest** possible **obtuse** angle ?

A.   90°   B.   89°   C.   179°   D.   91°   E.   180°

Question 37. If $3n = 11$ what would be the value of $12n$?

A.   6   B.   22   C.   33   D.   11   E.   44

Question 38.   What is **3.056 x 1000** ?

A.   3056   B.   30.56   C.   305.6   D.   3.056   E.   0.3056

Question 39. In a P.6 class there are **32** pupils. At Easter the teacher decides to give each child **8 small chocolate Rabbits** as a present.

The Chocolate rabbits come in **boxes of 24**.

What is the **least** number of **boxes** of Rabbits the teacher will need to buy ?

A.   4   B.   8   C.   12   D.   3   E.   11

Question 40. Cecil wanted to buy a pair of runners which cost **£60**.

He had saved **one quarter** of the total price and his mother gave him another **£21** towards the price .

What **fraction** of the total cost had Cecil **still** to get ?

A. $\dfrac{3}{4}$ B. $\dfrac{3}{5}$ C. $\dfrac{1}{4}$ D. $\dfrac{2}{5}$ E. $\dfrac{1}{2}$

Question 41. A single decker bus holds **45** passengers.

The bus is $\dfrac{3}{5}$ **empty**.

How many passengers **are** on the bus?

A.   18   B.   27   C.   36   D.   45   E.   9

Questions 42 & 43. The vertices of this regular **octagon** meet in the centre to create **8 identical isosceles** triangles.

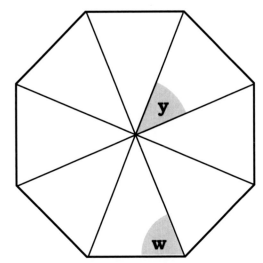

Question 42. What is the size of angle **y** ?

A.   60°   B.   67.5°   C.   72°   D.   30°   E.   45°

Question 43. What is the size of angle **w** ?

A.   37.5°   B.   72°   C.   135°   D.   67.5°   E.   45°

Question 44. Each of the squares in the grid is **1 cm by 1 cm.**

The dotted shape is made from a **square** and a **right-angle triangle**.

☐ = **1 sq. cm.**

What is the **area** of the **dotted section** of this shape ?

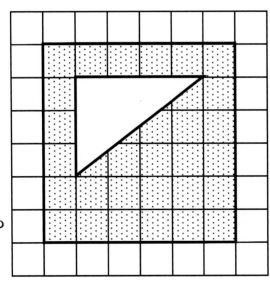

A. 30sq.cms   B. 24sq.cms   C. 36sq.cms   D. 42sq.cms   E. 6 sq.cms

10.

Question 45.   These are the temperatures recorded
at midday in one week last year.

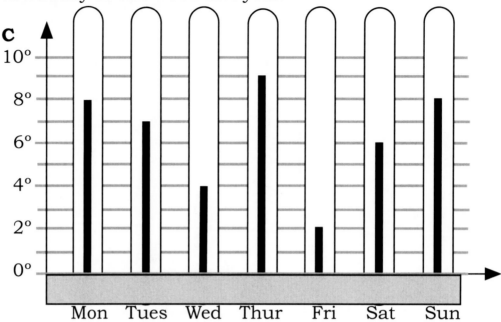

Between which TWO days was the **difference** in
temperatures the **greatest** ?

A.   Monday and Tuesday   B.   Wednesday and Thursday

C.   Friday and Sunday   D.   Friday and Thursday

E.   Saturday and Tuesday

NEW TRANSFER TESTS

MULTIPLE-CHOICE
MATHS
Practice Test 14

Guidance for completing this Test.

1. Read the questions carefully.

2. Do your working out thoroughly.

3. Read your answers carefully.

4. Choose what you think is the correct answer carefully.

5. Underline or circle the answer, immediately after the question.

6. Transfer the LETTER **A,B,C,D or E** to the answer sheet.

7. Make sure to mark the answer box like [—] not [✓].

8. Check carefully that you have transferred your correct answer.

9 . This test lasts for **45 minutes**.

PUPIL'S NAME _____

TOTAL MARK (Out of 45)	

MATHS (Multiple Choice)   Test 14.

Question 1.   A bag contains **4 Green** marbles, **3 Blue** marbles,

12 **Red** marbles and some **Pink** marbles.

The probability of taking a **Red** marble

from the bag at random is **"EVENS"**.

How many **Pink** marbles are there in the bag ?

A.   3   B.   4   C.   6   D.   5   E.   12

Question 2.   The 4 spinners are used to play a game.

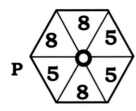 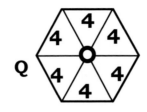 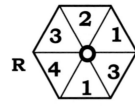 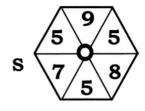

With which TWO spinners would you be **certain** to get a
number **greater than 4** ?

A.   **P & Q**   B.   **P & R**   C.   **Q & S**   D.   **R & S**   E.   **P & S**

Question 3.   As a **whole number** what is the size of

the **smallest possible obtuse** angle ?

A.   89°   B.   91°   C.   90°   D.   179°   E.   181°

Question 4.   The distance around a room is **24** metres.

The room is **TWICE as long** as it is **wide**.

What is the **length** of the room ?

A.   2 cms   B.   4 cms   C.   6 cms   D.   8 cms   E.   12 cms

Question 5.

The drawing is of a
large square of card with
a **small rectangle** beside it .
The dimensions are
shown in **centimetres**.

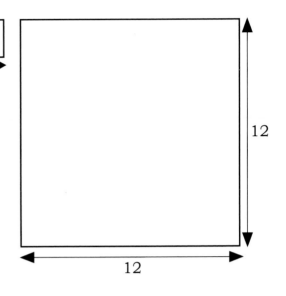

How many pieces the same size
as the **small rectangle**
can be cut from the **square** ?

A.   24   B.   4   C.   12   D.   48   E.   8

Question 6.   This function machine **trebles** the number and **adds 9**.

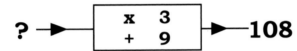

What number goes into the machine ?

A.   351   B.   23   C.   99   D.   39   E.   33

Question 7.

Black and white tiles
make a pattern on a floor.

Which **3 squares** must be
black so that the pattern
has exactly **2 lines** of symmetry ?

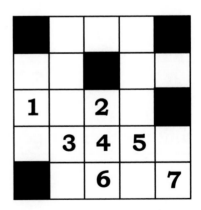

A. 1, 2, 7   B. 2, 4, 6   C. 3, 4, 5   D. 1, 4, 7   E. 5, 6, 3

Question 8.   Complete this calculation:- _____ **x 100 = 34.6**

A.   0.346   B.   3.46   C.   34.6   D.   346   E.   3460

2.

Question 9. If Janet has **3 pound** coins, **five 50 pence** coins, **seven 20 pence** coins, **nine 5 pence** coins and **eleven 2 pence** coins how much does she have in total ?

A. 35 p   B. £7.57   C. £17.57   D. £3.57   E. £1.57

Question 10. A local Council has **100** flower beds to plant.
They plant **386** bulbs in each bed.
In total how many bulbs does the Council plant ?

A. 386   B. 3860   C. 38600   D. 38   E. 386000

Question 11.

The Spinner is for
a game of **"Dare"**.
There are 3 sections,
YES, **NO** and **MAYBE**.
The Spinner will stop
at one of these 3.

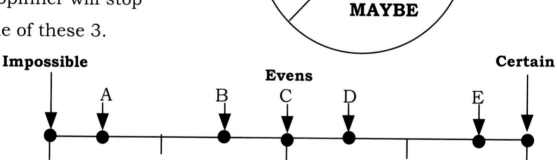

Which arrow on the probability scale shows the **probability** that the Spinner points towards **MAYBE** ?

Question 12. Which 3-dimensional solid has :-

> **5 faces,**
> **5 vertices and**
> **one face square**

A. cube   B. cuboid   C. sphere
D. square-based pyramid   E. triangular prism

3.

Question 13. Here is a pattern using equilateral triangles.

  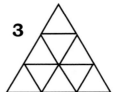 

How many triangles would there be in the **FOURTH** pattern ?

A.　10　　　B.　12　　　C.　14　　　D.　16　　　E.　25

Question 14.　　　　　　Look at the number line.

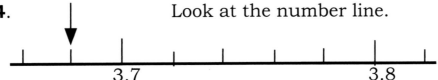

What number is the arrow pointing towards ?

A. 3.68　　B. 3.72　　C. 3.69　　D. 3.62　　E. 3.78

Question 15.　　　　Five shapes are shown here.

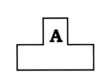  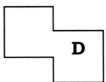

Which of these shapes has **exactly 5 internal** right angles ?

Question 16.　The heights of the 5 members of a family are shown.

Father	Mother	Son	Granny	Daughter
1.82 m	175 cms	1.49 m	1.65 m	152 cms

What is the **range** of these 5 heights ?

A. 33cms　　　B. 3.31 m　　　C. 1.82 m　　　D. 1.49　　　E.　7 cms

4.

Question 17. While in France the Evans family bought a football for **12 €uro** and a T-shirt for **18 €uro**.

Back home the football would cost **£10** and the T-shirt for **£15**.

How much would a **24 €uro** Football jersey cost in **£ pounds** ?

A.   £12   B.   £16   C.   £20   D.   £24   E.   £30

Question 18. Harry will be **w** years old in **4 years** time.
How old was he **5 years** ago, using **w** in your answer.

A. **5w**   B. **w + 5**   C. **5 - w**   D. **w - 9**   E. **w + 9**

Question 19. An ice skater spins round **3 and a half** revolutions.

Through how many degrees does the skater spin ?

A.   360°   B.   180°   C.   720°   D.   1080°   E.   1260°

Question 20. A motorcycle race track measures **6800 metres** long.
A race does **10 circuits** of the track.
What length is the race in **kilometres** ?

A. 10 kms   B. 6.8 kms   C. 68 kms   D. 680 kms   E. 16.8 kms

---

Question 21.   Which of these decimals is

smaller than $\frac{3}{4}$ but **bigger** than $\frac{1}{2}$?

A.   0.35   B.   0.45   C.   0.75   D.   0.55   E.   0.85

5.

Question 22.

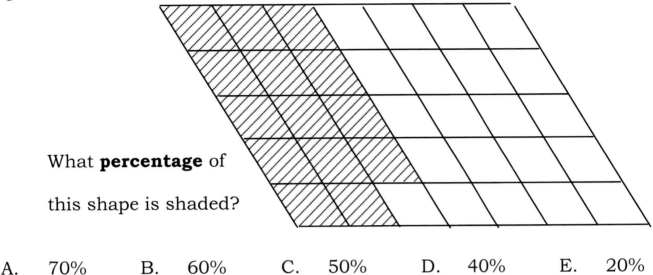

What **percentage** of this shape is shaded?

A.　70%　　　B.　60%　　　C.　50%　　　D.　40%　　　E.　20%

Question 23.

This is a drawing of a school corridor.

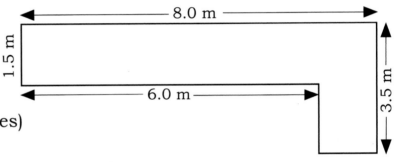

What **area** (in sq. metres) of tiles is needed to tile this corridor ?

A.　16　　　B.　12　　　C.　48　　　D.　28　　　E.　18

Question 24.　　**84**　　**76**　　**55**　　**83**　　**61**

Which of the numbers above has a **remainder of 5** when **divided by 7** ?

A.　84　　　B.　76　　　C.　55　　　D.　83　　　E.　61

Question 25.　If Alec is facing **North** and turns **anticlockwise** to face **South-west** through how many degrees has he moved ?

A.　90°　　　B.　135°　　　C.　180°　　　D.　270°　　　E.　225°

Question 26.   A length of rope measuring **7 . 02 metres**

is divided into **9** equal pieces.

What is the length of each piece ?

A. 63.18 m   B.   1.2 m   C.   0.78 m   D.   1.56 m   E.   6.12 m

---

Question 27.

Some of the nets will make
an open cubic box, like
the one shown.
The Shaded square is the **base**.

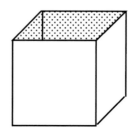

Which net would make an open box like the one shown ?

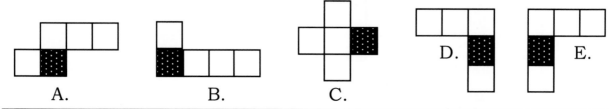

A.   B.   C.

Question 28.   Which number is **nearest** in value to **10** ?

A.   10.1   B.   9.99   C.   9.59   D.   9.09   E.   10.09

Question 29.   Kevin had **48** marbles. He lost **16** of them but then
won **twice as many** as he had lost.
How many has he now ?

A.   48   B.   16   C.   96   D.   32   E.   64

Question 30.   Bev gave Jill **half** of her sweets and was left with **36**.

How many sweets had Bev before sharing them ?

A.   18   B.   72   C.   45   D.   108   E.   9

Question 31. What is the **Perimeter** of a room which is

7.8 metres long and 5.6 metres wide ?

A. 13.4 m   B. 15.6 m   C. 11.2 m   D. 26.8 m   E. 3.9 m

Question 32. 400 grams of beef joint costs £3.20.

How much would 2 kilograms of the joint cost ?

A. £16   B. £8   C. £3.20   D. £6.40   E. £1.60

Question 33. Four parcels and their weights are shown.

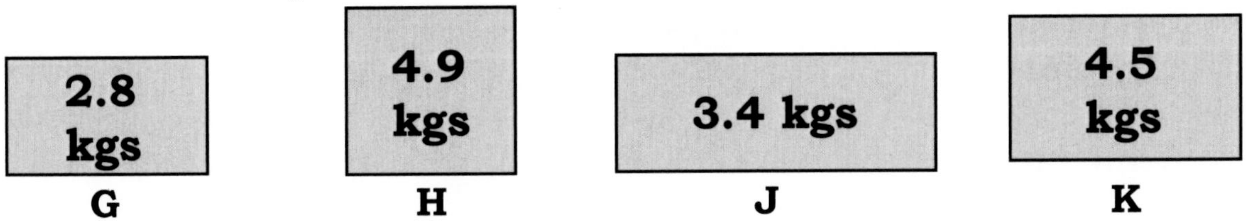

| 2.8 kgs | 4.9 kgs | 3.4 kgs | 4.5 kgs |
| G | H | J | K |

Which **TWO** parcels have a total weight of **8.3 kgs** ?

A. **G and H**   B. **G and J**   C. **G and K**   D. **H and J**   E. **J and K**

Question 34. 4 tins of **White** paint are mixed with 3 tins of **Black** paint to make 7 tins of **Grey** paint.

How many tins of **White** paint are needed to make 21 tins of **Grey** paint ?

A. 12   B. 9   C. 14   D. 7   E. 24

Question 35.

An **Isosceles** trapezium is shown.

What is the size of angle **t** ?

(diagram: isosceles trapezium with angle t at top left and 65° at bottom right)

A. 65°   B. 115°   C. 295°   D. 25°   E. 90°

8.

Question 36. After **halving** his real age Tom added **8 years** to it.

His age would be **18** years old .

What is Tom's **real age** ?

A. 4 B. 9 C. 13 D. 26 E. 20

Question 37. Packets of frozen chicken pieces don't all have the same number of chicken pieces.

CHICK FRIES **14 pieces**   CHICK FRIES **16 pieces**   CHICK FRIES **11 pieces**   CHICK FRIES **15 pieces**

Which number below is the **average (mean) number** of pieces for these **4 packets** ?

A. 12 B. 13 C. 14.5 D. 13.5 E. 14

Question 38.

This solid Cross-shape has a number of flat faces and a number of **external vertices**, some you can see and some hidden.

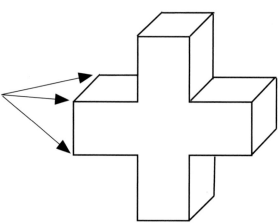

How many **external vertices** (those that can be seen and those hidden) in **total** does the cross-shape have ?

A. 2 B. 4 C. 8 D. 12 E. 16

Question 39.   A family holiday ended on
Wednesday, 4th March, 2009.

The holiday began **8 days** earlier on a **Tuesday**.

On what **date** did the holiday **begin** ?

A.   3rd March 2009
C.   23rd February 2009
E.   24th February 2009

B.   26th February 2009
D.   25th February 2009

Question 40.   A rectangle has an area of **72 sq. cms**.

If TWO of the sides are each **9 cms** long,

what is the length of each of the other sides ?

A. 27 cms   B. 9 cms   C. 8 cms   D. 36 cms   E. 18 cms

Question 41.   On a Farmers' Market stall at a Fair, Sally was selling
home-made cakes, pastries and shortcake.
She sold **60** cakes at **£1.50** each, **40** pastries at **20**
pence each and **100** shortcake at **9** pence each.
How much money did Sally get ?

A.   £90   B.   £300   C.   £9   D. £107   E.   £1.79

Question 42.   Five shapes are shown. One of them has an obtuse angle.

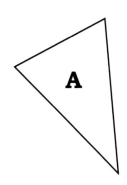
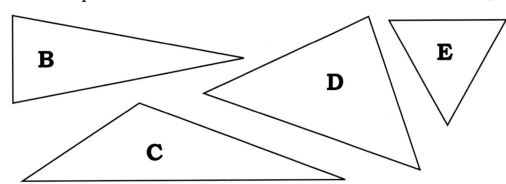

Which shape has an **obtuse** angle ?

10.

Question 43. An Addition calculation is shown below.
Fill in the missing digits to make the addition correct.

$$369 + 8\_5 = 1\_64$$

A. 9 and 2   B. 3 and 9   C. 9 and 4   D. 2 and 7   E. 3 and 6

Question 44. Arthur is saving to buy a bicycle which is costing **£170**.

He saves **£19** each week.

In **how many weeks** will he have

saved enough to buy the bicycle ?

A.   10   B.   12   C.   8   D.   9   E.   11

Question 45. The **arrow** shows the weight of a box of apples.

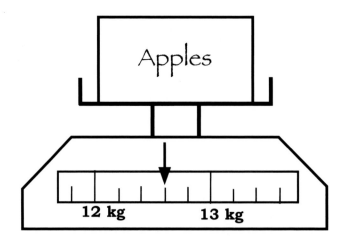

If another **800 grams** of apples are added to the
box what will the **total** weight be ?

A.   12.6 kg   B.   12.3 kg   C.   13.4 kg   D.   13 kg   E.   13.2 kg

---

SET 4 Blank Answer Sheets
MATHS test 13, MATHS test 14,
MATHS test 15, MATHS test 16.

Instructions for completing the Answer Sheet.

1. You must concentrate fully when recording your answers.

   --take your time when recording your answers--

   --make sure you have the correct answer number--

   --make sure you select the correct letter, A, B, C, D, E or N--

2. Use a pencil to mark your answer, A, B, C, D, E or N.

3. Mark your answer like this---- (A̶) (B) (C) (D) (E) (N)

   (A) (B) (C̶) (D) (E) (N)

   (A) (B) (C) (D) (E) (N̶)

   ALWAYS USE A HORIZONTAL (—) LINE

4. DO NOT MARK like this-- (A) (B) (C) (D̶) (E) (N)

   (A) (B) (C̶) (D) (E) (N)

   (A) (B̸) (C) (D) (E) (N)

   (A) (B) (C) (D) (E̶) (N)

5. If you make a mistake, rub out the line, select the correct answer and draw a line through the correct letter.

6. It might be an idea to answer 5 questions at a time and then record these 5 answers all at the same time.

7. When reading the questions you record the answers on the question paper. When you have completed 5 questions on the question paper you then record these on the Answer sheet. Proceed to record another 5 questions.

Mark the LETTER correctly. Eg. (C)--correct   (C)--incorrect

ANSWER SHEET

MATHS TEST 13

1	(A)(B)(C)(D)(E)	24	(A)(B)(C)(D)(E)
2	(A)(B)(C)(D)(E)	25	(A)(B)(C)(D)(E)
3	(A)(B)(C)(D)(E)	26	(A)(B)(C)(D)(E)
4	(A)(B)(C)(D)(E)	27	(A)(B)(C)(D)(E)
5	(A)(B)(C)(D)(E)	28	(A)(B)(C)(D)(E)
6	(A)(B)(C)(D)(E)	29	(A)(B)(C)(D)(E)
7	(A)(B)(C)(D)(E)	30	(A)(B)(C)(D)(E)
8	(A)(B)(C)(D)(E)	31	(A)(B)(C)(D)(E)
9	(A)(B)(C)(D)(E)	32	(A)(B)(C)(D)(E)
10	(A)(B)(C)(D)(E)	33	(A)(B)(C)(D)(E)
11	(A)(B)(C)(D)(E)	34	(A)(B)(C)(D)(E)
12	(A)(B)(C)(D)(E)	35	(A)(B)(C)(D)(E)
13	(A)(B)(C)(D)(E)	36	(A)(B)(C)(D)(E)
14	(A)(B)(C)(D)(E)	37	(A)(B)(C)(D)(E)
15	(A)(B)(C)(D)(E)	38	(A)(B)(C)(D)(E)
16	(A)(B)(C)(D)(E)	39	(A)(B)(C)(D)(E)
17	(A)(B)(C)(D)(E)	40	(A)(B)(C)(D)(E)
18	(A)(B)(C)(D)(E)	41	(A)(B)(C)(D)(E)
19	(A)(B)(C)(D)(E)	42	(A)(B)(C)(D)(E)
20	(A)(B)(C)(D)(E)	43	(A)(B)(C)(D)(E)
21	(A)(B)(C)(D)(E)	44	(A)(B)(C)(D)(E)
22	(A)(B)(C)(D)(E)	45	(A)(B)(C)(D)(E)
23	(A)(B)(C)(D)(E)		

ANSWER SHEET

MATHS TEST 14

1	(A)(B)(C)(D)(E)	24	(A)(B)(C)(D)(E)
2	(A)(B)(C)(D)(E)	25	(A)(B)(C)(D)(E)
3	(A)(B)(C)(D)(E)	26	(A)(B)(C)(D)(E)
4	(A)(B)(C)(D)(E)	27	(A)(B)(C)(D)(E)
5	(A)(B)(C)(D)(E)	28	(A)(B)(C)(D)(E)
6	(A)(B)(C)(D)(E)	29	(A)(B)(C)(D)(E)
7	(A)(B)(C)(D)(E)	30	(A)(B)(C)(D)(E)
8	(A)(B)(C)(D)(E)	31	(A)(B)(C)(D)(E)
9	(A)(B)(C)(D)(E)	32	(A)(B)(C)(D)(E)
10	(A)(B)(C)(D)(E)	33	(A)(B)(C)(D)(E)
11	(A)(B)(C)(D)(E)	34	(A)(B)(C)(D)(E)
12	(A)(B)(C)(D)(E)	35	(A)(B)(C)(D)(E)
13	(A)(B)(C)(D)(E)	36	(A)(B)(C)(D)(E)
14	(A)(B)(C)(D)(E)	37	(A)(B)(C)(D)(E)
15	(A)(B)(C)(D)(E)	38	(A)(B)(C)(D)(E)
16	(A)(B)(C)(D)(E)	39	(A)(B)(C)(D)(E)
17	(A)(B)(C)(D)(E)	40	(A)(B)(C)(D)(E)
18	(A)(B)(C)(D)(E)	41	(A)(B)(C)(D)(E)
19	(A)(B)(C)(D)(E)	42	(A)(B)(C)(D)(E)
20	(A)(B)(C)(D)(E)	43	(A)(B)(C)(D)(E)
21	(A)(B)(C)(D)(E)	44	(A)(B)(C)(D)(E)
22	(A)(B)(C)(D)(E)	45	(A)(B)(C)(D)(E)
23	(A)(B)(C)(D)(E)		

Multiple Choice Maths   Test 13 Answers.

1.	D	16.	A	31.	B
2.	A	17.	D	32.	E
3.	C	18.	D	33.	C
4.	E	19.	E	34.	D
5.	A	20.	A	35.	A
6.	C	21.	D	36.	C
7.	E	22.	B	37.	E
8.	D	23.	E	38.	A
9.	C	24.	B	39.	E
10.	A	25.	A	40.	D
11.	D	26.	C	41.	A
12.	E	27.	D	42.	E
13.	B	28.	D	43.	D
14.	A	29.	E	44.	A
15.	C	30.	A	45.	D

Multiple Choice Maths   Test 14 Answers.

1.	D	16.	A	31.	D
2.	E	17.	C	32.	A
3.	B	18.	D	33.	D
4.	D	19.	E	34.	A
5.	A	20.	C	35.	B
6.	E	21.	D	36.	E
7.	D	22.	D	37.	E
8.	A	23.	A	38.	E
9.	B	24.	E	39.	E
10.	C	25.	B	40.	C
11.	B	26.	C	41.	D
12.	D	27.	A	42.	C
13.	D	28.	B	43.	A
14.	A	29.	E	44.	D
15.	C	30.	B	45.	C

Multiple Choice Maths   **Test 15 Answers.**

1.	A	16.	E	31.	C
2.	C	17.	B	32.	D
3.	D	18.	D	33.	A
4.	A	19.	E	34.	E
5.	B	20.	B	35.	A
6.	D	21.	A	36.	B
7.	E	22.	B	37.	C
8.	B	23.	D	38.	A
9.	D	24.	A	39.	D
10.	A	25.	E	40.	C
11.	D	26.	A	41.	C
12.	D	27.	B	42.	A
13.	C	28.	D	43.	E
14.	B	29.	C	44.	E
15.	C	30.	B	45.	D

Multiple Choice Maths   Test 16 Answers.

1.	D	16.	A	31.	D
2.	A	17.	E	32.	A
3.	C	18.	D	33.	E
4.	E	19.	E	34.	A
5.	A	20.	D	35.	E
6.	D	21.	C	36.	D
7.	C	22.	E	37.	B
8.	B	23.	B	38.	C
9.	D	24.	D	39.	A
10.	B	25.	D	40.	C
11.	B	26.	D	41.	C
12.	D	27.	D	42.	D
13.	C	28.	C	43.	E
14.	D	29.	C	44.	B
15.	E	30.	A	45.	C

Mark the LETTER correctly. Eg. (C̶)--correct (Ø)--incorrect

ANSWER SHEET

MATHS TEST 15

1	(A)(B)(C)(D)(E)	24	(A)(B)(C)(D)(E)
2	(A)(B)(C)(D)(E)	25	(A)(B)(C)(D)(E)
3	(A)(B)(C)(D)(E)	26	(A)(B)(C)(D)(E)
4	(A)(B)(C)(D)(E)	27	(A)(B)(C)(D)(E)
5	(A)(B)(C)(D)(E)	28	(A)(B)(C)(D)(E)
6	(A)(B)(C)(D)(E)	29	(A)(B)(C)(D)(E)
7	(A)(B)(C)(D)(E)	30	(A)(B)(C)(D)(E)
8	(A)(B)(C)(D)(E)	31	(A)(B)(C)(D)(E)
9	(A)(B)(C)(D)(E)	32	(A)(B)(C)(D)(E)
10	(A)(B)(C)(D)(E)	33	(A)(B)(C)(D)(E)
11	(A)(B)(C)(D)(E)	34	(A)(B)(C)(D)(E)
12	(A)(B)(C)(D)(E)	35	(A)(B)(C)(D)(E)
13	(A)(B)(C)(D)(E)	36	(A)(B)(C)(D)(E)
14	(A)(B)(C)(D)(E)	37	(A)(B)(C)(D)(E)
15	(A)(B)(C)(D)(E)	38	(A)(B)(C)(D)(E)
16	(A)(B)(C)(D)(E)	39	(A)(B)(C)(D)(E)
17	(A)(B)(C)(D)(E)	40	(A)(B)(C)(D)(E)
18	(A)(B)(C)(D)(E)	41	(A)(B)(C)(D)(E)
19	(A)(B)(C)(D)(E)	42	(A)(B)(C)(D)(E)
20	(A)(B)(C)(D)(E)	43	(A)(B)(C)(D)(E)
21	(A)(B)(C)(D)(E)	44	(A)(B)(C)(D)(E)
22	(A)(B)(C)(D)(E)	45	(A)(B)(C)(D)(E)
23	(A)(B)(C)(D)(E)		

ANSWER SHEET

MATHS TEST 16

1	(A)(B)(C)(D)(E)	24	(A)(B)(C)(D)(E)
2	(A)(B)(C)(D)(E)	25	(A)(B)(C)(D)(E)
3	(A)(B)(C)(D)(E)	26	(A)(B)(C)(D)(E)
4	(A)(B)(C)(D)(E)	27	(A)(B)(C)(D)(E)
5	(A)(B)(C)(D)(E)	28	(A)(B)(C)(D)(E)
6	(A)(B)(C)(D)(E)	29	(A)(B)(C)(D)(E)
7	(A)(B)(C)(D)(E)	30	(A)(B)(C)(D)(E)
8	(A)(B)(C)(D)(E)	31	(A)(B)(C)(D)(E)
9	(A)(B)(C)(D)(E)	32	(A)(B)(C)(D)(E)
10	(A)(B)(C)(D)(E)	33	(A)(B)(C)(D)(E)
11	(A)(B)(C)(D)(E)	34	(A)(B)(C)(D)(E)
12	(A)(B)(C)(D)(E)	35	(A)(B)(C)(D)(E)
13	(A)(B)(C)(D)(E)	36	(A)(B)(C)(D)(E)
14	(A)(B)(C)(D)(E)	37	(A)(B)(C)(D)(E)
15	(A)(B)(C)(D)(E)	38	(A)(B)(C)(D)(E)
16	(A)(B)(C)(D)(E)	39	(A)(B)(C)(D)(E)
17	(A)(B)(C)(D)(E)	40	(A)(B)(C)(D)(E)
18	(A)(B)(C)(D)(E)	41	(A)(B)(C)(D)(E)
19	(A)(B)(C)(D)(E)	42	(A)(B)(C)(D)(E)
20	(A)(B)(C)(D)(E)	43	(A)(B)(C)(D)(E)
21	(A)(B)(C)(D)(E)	44	(A)(B)(C)(D)(E)
22	(A)(B)(C)(D)(E)	45	(A)(B)(C)(D)(E)
23	(A)(B)(C)(D)(E)		

NEW TRANSFER TESTS

MULTIPLE-CHOICE

MATHS

Practice Test 15

Guidance for completing this Test.

1.   Read the questions carefully.

2.   Do your working out thoroughly.

3.   Read your answers carefully.

4.   Choose what you think is the correct answer carefully.

5.   Underline or circle the answer, immediately after the question.

6.   Transfer the LETTER **A,B,C,D or E** to the answer sheet.

7.   Make sure to mark the answer box like [—] not [/].

8.   Check carefully that you have transferred your correct answer.

9 .   This test lasts for **45 minutes.**

PUPIL'S NAME _____

TOTAL MARK (Out of 45)	

MATHS (Multiple Choice)   Test 15.

Question 1.   Regular Hexagon spinners are used to begin a table game.

Amie goes first if she throws Blue.   **B = blue**
Cora goes first if she spins Yellow.   **Y = yellow**
Dawn goes first if she spins Pink.   **P = pink**

Which spinner would be **fair** to all three players ?

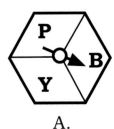    

A.   B.   C.   D.   E.

Question 2.   Which of the following has an answer of **36** ?

A.   30% of 360   B.   0.75 of 100   C. $\frac{4}{9}$ of 81

D.   60% of 70   E. $\frac{5}{8}$ of 64

Questions 3 & 4.   Bart and Joe are building a garden wall.

It takes Bart **5 hours** to build a quarter of the wall.

It takes Joe **4 hours** to build 20% of the wall.

Each of the men have to build **half** the wall.

Question 3.   How long does it take Bart to build **his half** of the wall ?

A.   5 hrs   B.   8 hrs   C.   20 hrs   D.   10 hrs   E.   4 hrs

Question 4.   How long does it take Joe to build **his half** of the wall ?

A.   10 hrs   B.   8 hrs   C.   20 hrs   D.   5 hrs   E.   4 hrs

1.

Questions 5 & 6.

The drawing shows the
Big Wheel in Belfast.
Fay is in the carriage at **10**.
Tom is in the carriage at **7**.
The wheel moves in a
clockwise direction through
'three-quarters' of a revolution.

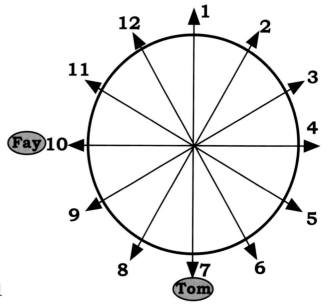

Question 5.   At which point does
Tom's carriage **stop** ?

A. 6   B. 4   C. 1
D. 10   E. 3

Question 6.   If Fay's carriage moves from its present position
anti-clockwise to **number 5** through how
many degrees does it move ?

A. 60°   B. 120°   C. 90°   D. 150°   E. 210°

Question 7.   Which **quadrilateral** has only **one pair** of equal angles

and only **one line** of reflective symmetry ?

A. rhombus   B. parallelogram   C. square
D. trapezium   E. kite

Question 8.   On a map of Ireland the scale is **1 : 300,000**.

Two towns on the map are **2 centimetres** apart.

What **real** distance is there between these two towns ?

A. 300,000 metres   B. 6 kms   C. 60 kms
D. 6000 kms   E. 600,000 metres

Question 9.   What is **65,875 ÷ 100** ?

A. 6587.5   B. 6.5875   C. 65.875   D. 658.75   E. 0.65875

Question 10. The three angles in an Isosceles triangle are **P, Q** and **R**.

The size of angle **Q** is **65°**.

Angles **P** and **Q** differ in size by **15°**.

What is the size of angle **R** ?

A.   65°   B.   50°   C.   115°   D.   80°   E.   130°

Question 11. If **31 x 45 + 30 = 1425** what would the answer

to **31 x 45 - 30** be ?

A.   1425   B.   1400   C.   1455   D.   1365   E.   1395

Question 12. There are **12 eggs** in a dozen.
How many eggs are there in **5 and a half dozen** ?

A.   6   B.   60   C.   17   D.   66   E.   33

Question 13.

A triangle and a square
are drawn on the grid.
Each square on the grid
is **1cm** by **1cm**.

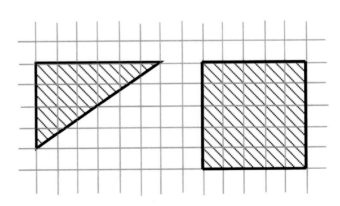

What is the **difference** in their **areas** in square centimetres ?

A.   24   B.   12   C.   13   D.   25   E.   1

3.

Question 14. A theatre seats **600** people. **385** tickets are sold in advance while another **146** tickets are sold at the door. How many **empty** seats were there in the theatre ?

A.   165   B.   69   C.   239   D.   454   E.   169

Questions 15 to 17.   In a bicycle race the riders were wearing numbers between **6** and **40**.

Question 15. If the winner was wearing a number which is both a multiple of **8** and a **square number**, what was the number on the winner's jersey ?

A.   6   B.   40   C.   16   D.   32   E.   36

Question 16. The runner-up in the race wore a jersey with a number which was a factor of **40**. In which group are the numbers which could have been worn by the runner-up ?

A.   12, 10, 20   B.   16, 10, 30   C.   20, 40, 80
D.   40, 60, 80   E.   8, 10, 20

Question 17. The last rider to cross the finishing line wore a number which is the **highest prime number** between **6** and **40**. What is this number ?

A. 39   B. 37   C. 35   D. 33   E.   31

Question 18. Complete this measuring sentence :-

$$125 \text{ grams} + 5.35 \text{ kgs} = \underline{\hspace{2cm}} \text{ grams}$$

A. 660   B. 1320   C. 5160   D. 5475   E. 560

4.

Questions 19 & 20. The passengers on a Holiday Tour plane from Belfast to Spain are from 3 Pensioners clubs, named **Young at Heart**, **Silver Wings** and **Golden Years**. All seats were occupied.

Young at Heart booked $\frac{3}{8}$ of the seats.

Silver Wings had booked $\frac{3}{8}$ of the seats.

Golden Years had the rest which accounted for **60** seats.

Question 19. What **fraction** of the seats had **Golden Years** booked?

A. $\frac{3}{8}$ B. $\frac{5}{8}$ C. $\frac{1}{3}$ D. $\frac{1}{8}$ E. $\frac{1}{4}$

Question 20. What was the **total number** of seats in the plane?

A.   60   B.   240   C.   160   D.   120   E.   300

Question 21.

A quadrilateral is drawn here.

The angles are **p**, **q**, **r** and **s**.

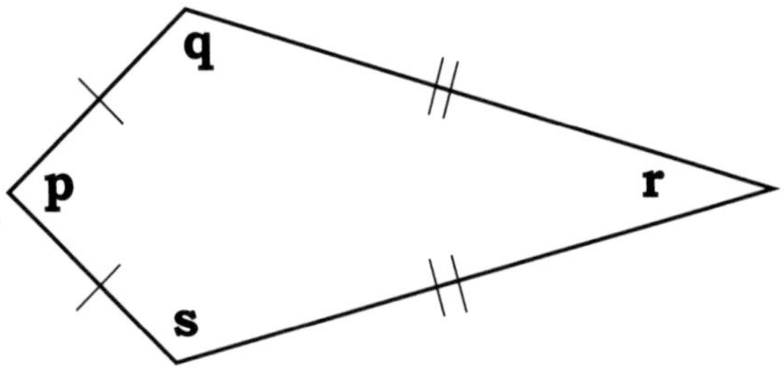

Which two angles are **equal** ?

A. **s** and **q**   B. **p** and **r**   C. **p** and **s**   D. **q** and **r**   E. **r** and **s**

Question 22.   Here is a list of numbers:-

-6   -4   -1   0   2   5   6

What is the **sum** of all the numbers ?

A.   -2   B.   2   C.   -3   D.   24   E.   12

5.

Question 23.   There are 4 **Black** marbles in this bag.

You want to make sure that it will be **more likely** to pick a **White** marble from the bag than a **Black** one.

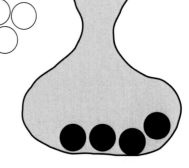

What is the **minimum** number of these **White** marbles that needs to be put into the bag to ensure that you are more likely to pick a **White** marble rather than a black one ?

A.   7   B.   6   C.   4   D.   5   E.   3

Questions 24 & 25.   The cubic box has sides of **20** cms. It is to be filled with wooden cubic bricks of side **5** cms as in the diagram.

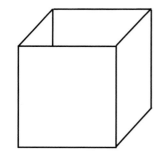

Drawings not to scale

5 cms

Question 24.   How many **5cm** cubic bricks will it hold ?

A.   64   B.   164   C.   8   D.   100   E.   25

Question 25.   What is the volume of the box in **cubic cms** ?

A.   20   B.   400   C.   800   D.   1000   E.   8000

Question 26.   A mother buys **3** pairs of shorts at **£9.50** each and **3** shirts at **£4.99** each.

How much change has she out of **£50** ?

A. £6.53   B.   £35.51   C.   £21.50   D.   £40.50   E.   £39.99

Questions 27 & 28..   The Square diagram below represents the
Makes of **180** cars in a supermarket car park.

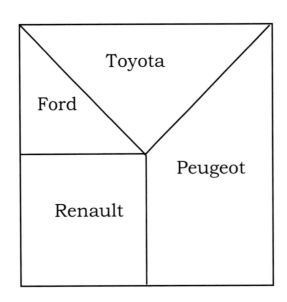

Question 27.   How many **Toyota** cars are in the car park?

A.   180   B.   45   C.   60   D.   90   E.   30

Question 28.   What **fraction** of the total cars are made by **Peugeot**?

A. $\dfrac{1}{8}$ B. $\dfrac{1}{6}$ C. $\dfrac{1}{4}$ D. $\dfrac{3}{8}$ E. $\dfrac{1}{2}$

Question 29.   Mark uses three different numbers to
make a **product of 54.**

His **first** number is the **square of 3.**

His **second** is a factor of **12.**

His **third** is the **smallest Prime number.**

What are Mark's 3 numbers?

A. **3, 6, 1**   B. **9, 4, 2**   C. **9, 3, 2**   D. **9, 12, 2**   E. **3, 6, 5**

Question 30. The last day of **February 2000** was a Friday. On what day was the **7th March 2000** ?

A. Thursday   B. Friday   C. Saturday   D. Sunday   E. Monday

---

Question 31. William left London airport at **19:45 GMT** and arrived at Hong Kong the **next** day at **07:15 GMT**.
How long did the journey last ?

A. 11 hrs   B. 10 hrs   C. $11\frac{1}{2}$ hrs   D. $12\frac{1}{2}$ hrs   E. 13 hrs

---

Questions 32 & 33. The table below shows the prices of three different cereals at five different shops.

	CASH	**DOUGH**	**MONEY**	**BREAD**	**DOSH**
Frishies	£2.00	£2.20	£2.00	£1.90	£2.50
Crushies	£1.60	£1.80	£1.50	£1.55	£2.00
Marshies	£2.50	£2.35	£3.00	£2.15	£3.00

Question 32. Mrs. Marley buys **one** packet of **Marshies** and **one** packet of **Frishies**. The total cost was **£4.05**.

From which shop did she buy these ?

A.   **CASH**   B.   **DOUGH**   C.   **MONEY**   D.   **BREAD**   E.   **DOSH**

Question 33. Mrs. Hurley buys **Two** packets of each of the cereals.

The total cost was **£12 . 20**.

From which shop did she buy these ?

A.   **CASH**   B.   **DOUGH**   C.   **MONEY**   D.   **BREAD**   E.   **DOSH**

8.

Question 34. Calculate :- $4^2 \times 3^2 + 20 =$ _____

A.   27   B.   39   C.   45   D.   32   E.   164

Question 35 to 37. Look at the net of a **Square-based Pyramid** and answer the questions which follow.

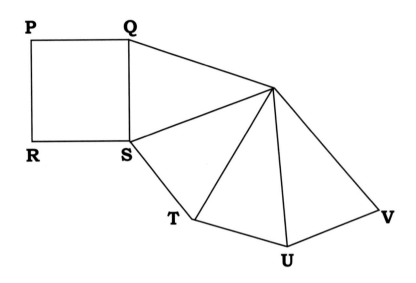

Question 35. When the net is made into a pyramid which point will meet **P** ?

A.   **U**   B.   **V**   C.   **T**   D.   **S**   E.   **Q**

Question 36. Which point will meet **Q** ?

A.   **U**   B.   **V**   C.   **T**   D.   **S**   E.   **Q**

Question 37. Which point will meet **R** ?

A.   **U**   B.   **V**   C.   **T**   D.   **S**   E.   **Q**

Question 38. If the value of **P** is **5** what is the value of **3P - 6** ?

A.   9   B.   29   C.   21   D.   35   E.   90
                                          9.

Question 39. Which **pair** of temperatures have a difference of **11°C** ?

A.   3°C   and   8°C   B.   6°C   and   16°C   C.   11°C   and   1°C

D.   -6°C   and   5°C   E.   -9°C   and   -2°C

Question 40. If a bag contains $3\frac{3}{4}$ kgs of potatoes what weight of potatoes is added to it to make the weight $5\frac{1}{2}$ kgs ?

A. $1\frac{1}{4}$ kg   B. $2\frac{1}{4}$ kg   C. $1\frac{3}{4}$ kg   D. $\frac{1}{2}$ kg   E. $\frac{3}{4}$ kg

---

Question 41. There are **35** pupils in a class. **2 fifths** go home for lunch. **One fifth** take a packed lunch. The rest go to the canteen. How many go to the canteen ?

A.   35   B.   7   C.   14   D.   21   E.   70

Question 42. Sally takes violin lessons for a year in **3** terms, each term lasting **12** weeks. If the fee for each lesson is **£2.50** how much does Sally pay for the year's lessons ?

A.   £90   B.   £30   C.   £7.50   D.   £60   E.   £10

Questions 43.

The plan of a dining table is a regular hexagon.

The scale of the drawing is :- **1 : 50**

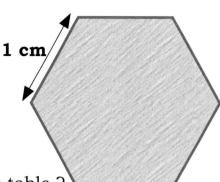

1 cm

What is the **actual perimeter** of the table ?

A. 30 cm   B. 100 cm   C. 1 metre   D. 6 metres   E. 3 metres

Question 44. Four of the shapes have the **same perimeter**.

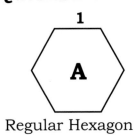
Regular Hexagon

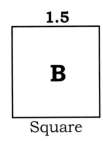
Square

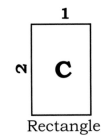
Rectangle

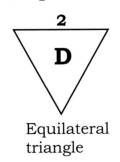
Equilateral triangle

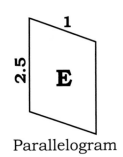
Parallelogram

All measurements are in **metres.**

Which shape has a **different perimeter** ?

_____

Question 45. **F, G, H** and **J** are vertices of a square.

F, G and **H** are marked on the grid.

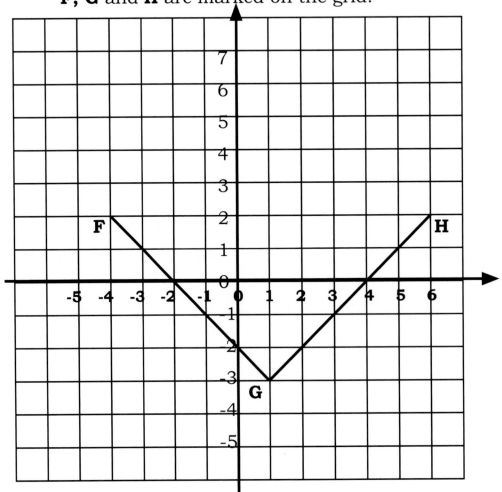

What are the coordinates of the fourth vertex, **J** ?

A.   (1, -3)   B.   (1, 4)   C.   (6, 2)   D.   (1, 7)   E.   (1, 6)

11.

NEW TRANSFER TESTS

MULTIPLE-CHOICE

MATHS

Practice Test 16

Guidance for completing this Test.

1. Read the questions carefully.

2. Do your working out thoroughly.

3. Read your answers carefully.

4. Choose what you think is the correct answer carefully.

5. Underline or circle the answer, immediately after the
    question.

6. Transfer the LETTER **A,B,C,D or E** to the answer sheet.

7. Make sure to mark the answer box like [—] not [/].

8. Check carefully that you have transferred your correct answer.

9 . This test lasts for **45 minutes.**

PUPIL'S NAME _____

TOTAL MARK (Out of 45)	

MATHS (Multiple Choice)

Question 1.

The graph shows how to convert kilometres to miles. How many miles is **400 kms** ?

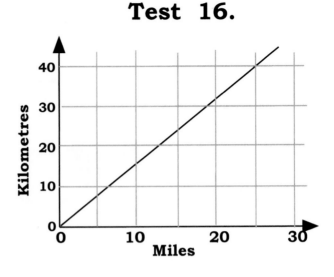

A. 800   B. 400
C. 50   D. 250
E. 25

Questions 2 to 4.   The Heights of mountains and other world features are determined by **"sea level"** which is **"zero metres high"**. For example Mount Everest is 8848 metres **above** **"sea level"**. Some places in the world are **below "sea level"**.

The heights of a number of places in the world are :-
Mt. Everest...8848 metres   Ben Nevis (Scotland)...1343 metres
Eiffel Tower...300 metres   SEA LEVEL..................0
London Underground (- 30 metres).....below sea level
Death Valley Bottom (- 86 metres).....below sea level

Question 2.   What is the **difference** between the heights of the Eiffel Tower and Ben Nevis ?

A. 1043 m   B. 1643 m   C. 43 m   D. 300 m   E. 1343 m

Question 3.   What is the **distance** from the bottom of Death Valley to the top of Ben Nevis ?

A. 1343 m   B. 1257 m   C. 1429   D. -86 m   E. -1343 m

Question 4.   If a rock climber was on a ledge **30** metres from the **bottom** of Death Valley how far is he **below** sea-level?

A. 30 m   B. 86 m   C. -30   D. -116   E. 56 m

1.

Question 5. Which of the following values is the **smallest** ?

A. **0 . 675**   B. $\dfrac{3}{4}$ C. **68%**   D. **0.7**   E. $\dfrac{4}{5}$

Question 6. The **Mean** number of sweets in **5** large boxes is **125**.
The numbers of sweets in **4** of the boxes are :-

    128   **137**   **145**   **116**

How many sweets are in the **5th** box ?

A.   145   B.   128   C.   137   D.   99   E.   116

Question 7. Triangular tiles are used in this sequence.

Pattern
number 1

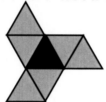

Pattern
number 2

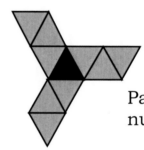

Pattern
number 3

How many grey tiles are in **Pattern number 4** ?

A.   8   B.   10   C.   12   D.   13   E.   14

Question 8. If $y = \frac{1}{2}x$ which of the following is **incorrect** ?

A. $y = x \div 2$ B. $y = 2x$ C. $x \div y = 2$
D. $x = 2y$ E. $y \div x = 0.5$

Question 9. Complete this calculation **34.7 ÷ 100** = ———

A.   347.0   B.   34.7   C.   3.47   D.   0.347   E.   3470

2.

Question 10. Five **regular** shapes are shown.
The **internal** angles of each of them are equal.

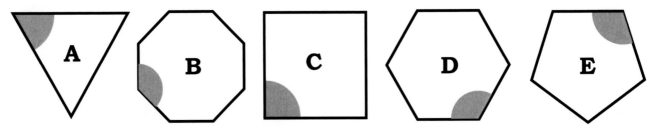

Which of the marked angles is the **largest** ?

Question 11. Of **220** bulbs planted in an hotel flower bed $\frac{2}{5}$ of them were killed by the frost.

How many bulbs **survived** ?

A.   44   B.   132   C.   88   D.   176   E.   440

Question 12. A **square** and an **equilateral triangle** are joined together.
What is the size of the angle marked **t** ?

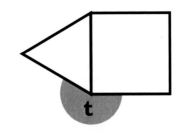

A.   60°   B.   90°   C.   150°   D.   210°   E.   180°

Question 13. Janice has **3 hours** free time on a Friday evening.
She spends **45 minutes** reading.
What **percentage** of the 3 hours does she spend reading ?

A.   60%   B.   30%   C.   25%   D.   20%   E.   15%

Question 14. What is **40%** of **4 hours** ?

A. 60 mins   B. 40 mins   C. 48 mins   D. 96 mins   E. 72 mins

Question 15. A glass holds **200 mls** of water.

To stay healthy adults need about **1 . 8 litres** of water per day.

How many glasses would an adult need to drink ?

A.   18   B.   8   C.   6   D.   10   E.   9

Questions 16 to 18.   A city centre Theatre has 3 levels of admission tickets.

Stalls ---- £39   **Balcony ---- £25**   **Gallery ---- £19**

Question 16.   How many **Gallery** tickets can be bought for **£200** ?

A.   10   B.   12   C.   16   D.   20   E.   30

Question 17.   How many **Balcony** tickets can be bought for **£300**?

A.   30   B.   10   C.   16   D.   20   E.   12

Question 18.   Jane buys **two** tickets for the **Stalls**.

She pays for them with **two £50** notes.

How much change does she get ?

A.   £100   B.   £50   C.   £11   D.   £22   E.   £178

Question 19.   What time is missing from this mathematical sentence?
_____ +   **35 mins**   =   **07:15**

A.   07:50   B.   06:20   C.   07:20   D.   07:05   E.   06:40

4.

Question 20.   Hannah bought TWO books for **£20**.

One of them cost **3 times** as much as the other.

How much was the more expensive book ?

A.   £20   B.   £5   C.   £23   D.   £15   E.   £6

Question 21.   Cards with shapes are shown. The cards are turned over and one is picked at random.

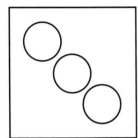 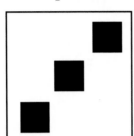 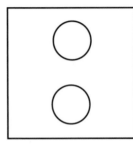 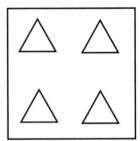

Which of the following probabilities is **incorrect** ?

A.   The probability of picking a card with **squares** on it is **0.25**.

B.   The probability of picking a card with **3 shapes** on it is **0.50**.

C.   The probability of picking a card with **black circles** on it is $\frac{1}{4}$.

D.   The probability of picking a card with **white shapes** on it is **0.75**.

E.   The probability of picking a card with **triangles** on it is **25%**.

Question 22.

Part of the reflection of a shape is shown.

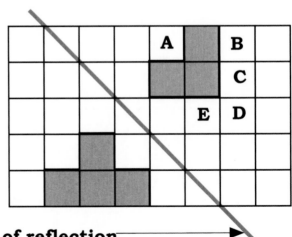

Which **square** needs to be **shaded** to complete the reflection ?

A.   B.   C.   D.   E.

Question 23.

Drawings of two flags
are shown.
Each has a shaded part.

By how much is the shaded
area of **Flag 2 bigger** than
the shaded area of **Flag 1** ?

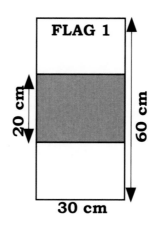 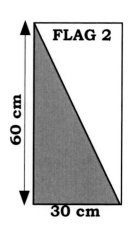

A. 600 sq.cms	B. 300 sq. cms	C. 1800 sq. cms
D. 900 sq. cms	E. 1200 sq. cms	

Question 24. Colm needs a piece of plywood, **0.78 metres**

wide and **1.73 metres** long.

Plywood is sold in the standard sizes below.

Which of the standard sizes should Colm buy to

have as little plywood as possible left over ?

A. 0.7 m x 1.7 m	B. 1.7 m x 0.9 m	C. 1.0 m x 2.0 m
D. 0.8 m x 1.8 m	E. 1.7 m x 0.8 m	

Question 25. There are **4 and a half litres** of oil in a car engine.
How many **millilitres** of oil are in the engine ?

A. 45 mls   B. 450 mls   C. 4.5 mls   D. 4500 mls   E. 4000 mls

---

Question 26.

A dice is numbered **1 to 6**.

Opposite faces of a dice **add** up to **7**.

Which face on the net of the cube

has the **5 dots** (●) on it?

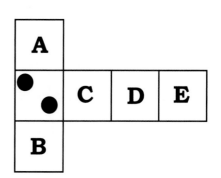

6.

Question 27. In a family shopping basket there were

6 cartons of Juice costing **£1.69** each and

4 packets of Cereal costing **£2.46** each.

What is the **total cost** of the Juice and the Cereal ?

A. £10.14   B. £9.84   C. £1.23   D. £19.98   E. £24.60

Question 28.

How many **light grey** triangles in total
are there in this design ?

A. 9   B. 8   C. 7
D. 10   E. 11

Question 29. If the price of **3** tickets for a

concert cost **£20** how much

would you pay for **12** concert tickets ?

A. £40   B. £15   C. £80   D. £60   E. £20

Question 30. If it cost **£117** to lay a path **9** metres long how much
would it cost to lay a path **12** metres long?

A. £156   B. £117   C. £88.50   D. £39   E. £13

Question 31. If sweets cost **85 pence** for **200 grams** how much
would **1 . 4 kilograms** cost ?

A. 85 p   B. £85   C. £4.25   D. £5.95   E. £14

Question 32. The light from the sun takes **502 seconds** to reach the earth.
How long is this in **minutes and seconds** ?

A.   8 mins 22 secs   B.   5 mins 2 secs   C.   2 mins 50 secs
D.   25 mins   E.   2 mins 51 secs

Questions 33 & 34.

Number cards showing 5 different digits are seen below.

2 1 6 9 5

Each digit can be used once to make the number 2 1 6 9 5

Question 33. What is the **smalles**t number that can be made from these digits ?

A.   16259   B.   15269   C.   25691   D.   51296   E.   12569

Question 34. What is the **largest** number that can be made from these digits ?

A.   96521   B.   65219   C.   52196   D.   21965   E.   19652

Question 35. The price of 1 packet of Oatsy Cereal is **99 pence**.

There is a special offer on Oatsy Cereal.

You can buy **3 for the price of 2**.

What is the cost of **1 packet** of the cereal in the special offer ?

A.   99 p   B.   £1.98   C.   £3.96   D.   £2.97   E.   66 p

Question 36. A glass holds **150 mls** of water.
A large jug holds **3 litres** of water.

How many **150 ml glasses** could be filled from this jug ?

A. 3   B. 150   C. 50   D. 20   E. 10

8.

Question 37.

What is the area of this diamond
shape on the **centimetre-squared** grid ?
The answer will be square centimetres.

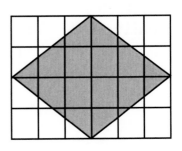

A.   24   B.   12   C.   48   D.   6   E.   18

Question 38.   These percentages, **20%, 90%, 40%, 75%, 10%**
are to be written into the boxes on the number line.

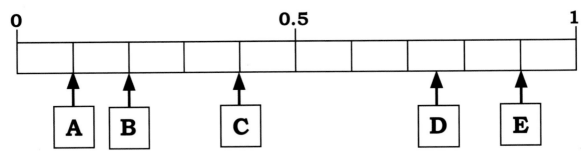

In which box would **40%** be placed ?

Question 39.   Steak costs **£8.59** for a **kilogram**.

How much, to the nearest penny,

would **200 grams** of the steak cost ?

A.   £1.72   B.   £1.71   C.   £8.60   D.   £0.86   E.   £1.70

Question 40.

Use the given calculation to find
the answer to the calculation below :-

$$36 \text{ x } 62 = 2232$$

$$36 \text{ x } 31 = \underline{\hspace{2cm}}$$

A.   4464   B.   2232   C.   1116   D.   558   E.   67

Question 41.   If **g** + **14** = **21**

what is the value of **3g** ?

A.   7   B.   14   C.   21   D.   35   E.   28

Questions 42 & 43. Drawings of two cuboids of the **same volume** are shown below.

Cuboid 1   **Cuboid 2**

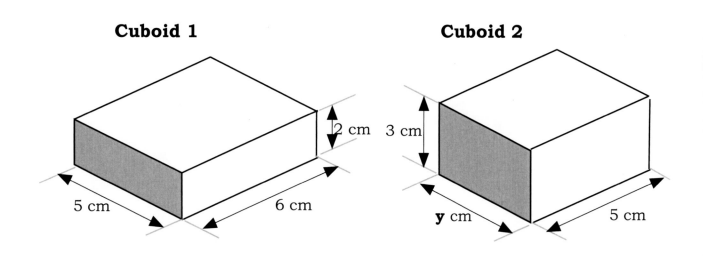

5 cm   2 cm   6 cm   3 cm   y cm   5 cm

Question 42.   What is the volume of **Cuboid 1** in **cubic cms** ?

A.   30   B.   12   C.   10   D.   60   E.   13

Question 43.   What is the length of the dimension **y** in **Cuboid 2** ?

A. 2 cms   B. 6 cms   C. 3 cms   D. 5 cms   E. 4 cms

10.

Question 44. A Winter temperature in Aberdeen was **-7°C**.

There was a **difference** of **12°C** between the Aberdeen temperature and that of Lisbon.

If it was **warmer** in Lisbon what was the Lisbon temperature ?

A.   19°C   B.   5°C   C.   -19°C   D.   -5°C   E.   12°C

Question 45.   Four straight pieces of metal are joined together as in the drawing.

There are TWO sets of **parallel** lines.

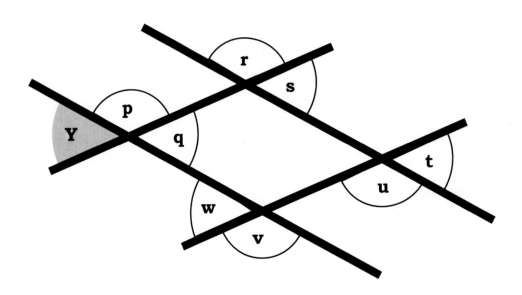

Which **pair** of angles are exactly the same size as angle **Y** ?

A.   **p** and **q**   B.   **r** and **s**   C.   **q** and **w**

D.   **v** and **u**   E.   **s** and **u**